Introductory Level
PHOTOCOPIABLE
WORKSHEETS
Spelling Made

Easy

Multi Sensory Structured Phonics

Best Selling Series by
Violet Brand

Published by BrandBooks

BrandBooks PO Box 367 Aylesbury Bucks HP22 4LJ England

Spelling Made Easy Worksheets Introductory Level
First published in the United Kingdom in 1987
Second impression 1988
Third impression 1990
Fourth impression 1991
Fifth impression 1992
Sixth impression 1992
Seventh impression 1993
Eighth impression 1994
Ninth impression 1994
Tenth impression 1995
by Egon Publishers Ltd.

Original copyright © Egon Publishers Ltd
and Violet Brand, 1987
ISBN 0 905858 41 7

Copyright assigned to BrandBooks
(a division of G & M Brand Publications Ltd) and Violet Brand 2002

ISBN 1-904421-04-0

Illustrated by Juanita Duffett

Introductory Level Work Sheets

Contents

Guide-lines for teachers	1
a	3
o	4
i	5
e	6
u	7
ck	8
ee	9
oo	10
ar	11
or	12
sh	13
ch	14
th	15
a-e	16
i-e	17
o-e	18
u-e	19
ai	20
oa	21
ir	22
ou	23
ea (ē)	24
ay	25
ing	26
ur	27
aw	28
oi	29
er	30
all	31
y (ē)	32
ea (ĕ)	33
ow	34
igh	35
a (ar)	36
y (ī)	37
o (ŭ)	38
ow (ō)	39
Blank picture boxes	40

Sad Gran

WORKSHEETS TO ACCOMPANY SPELLING MADE EASY
INTRODUCTORY LEVEL — FAT SAM

Guide-lines for Teachers

Teaching Points

Spelling in isolation is not enough. The word building skills acquired must be integrated into literacy generally. For a few children, this will happen automatically, but for others, tasks which will gently edge them along the path, will be essential. Constant reinforcement will be necessary and this can tax even the most imaginative teacher.

The aims of these worksheets are to ensure –

(a) that word families are not only identified in the spelling process, but also in reading;

(b) that word chunks are speedily recognised in tracking print;

(c) that information carried in print is understood, remembered and used;

(d) that recently acquired word families can be recalled whenever necessary;

(e) that literacy knowledge acquired can be utilised in proof reading.

These are *thinking* activities which will hopefully form useful, automatic habits for the future.

Pictures

When the children are asked to draw pictures, more will be required than is specifically asked for. This extra information is contained in the stories. When looking at the pictures afterwards, make sure that colours and activities relate to the relevant passage – not to a previous one.

Later in life the children will be required to give their responses in words. At this stage, pictures can reveal powers of comprehension.

If, with the weaker readers in a class, a group situation is used, or if parents are preparing the reading at home, encourage the information from the children, so that the picture is "talked through" from the print, until this stage is no longer required.

Paper should be supplied for the pictures and the sentences, which can be inserted into a "Sad Gran" file.

Sentences

Some children will write the required sentence easily alone. (Do ensure that complete sentences are used, including capital letters and punctuation). Others might need to build their sentences first in plastic letters and have them approved, before writing.

Labelling

When children are asked to write the label for a picture, make sure that they give all that is required, including correct numbers and plurals.

In order that there should be no confusion over the appropriate label, the following information is given *for the teacher.*

Labels can be discussed, but the following words must *not* be written down for the children to copy – otherwise the whole object of this section is defeated.

a	**or**	**oa**	**all**
tap jam bag	horse broom frog	coat road boat	small ball, big ball, brick wall
flag bat hand	forks fork clock	loaf soap toast	tall tree, small tree, three balls
o	**sh**	**ir**	**y (ē)**
cot fox dot	fish dish storm	girl skirt shirt	sad happy
box frog dog	arm sheep tick	brush bird birds	grumpy dirty
i	**ch**	**ou**	**ea (ĕ)**
six king fist	chin mugs brush	mouse house horse	bread sink ladder
sink lips hill	brick chips bed	shirt clouds soap	toe head claws
e	**th**	**ea(ē)**	**ow**
ten men belt	thin man, three, three stars	peas seat teapot	cow, empty bus, bus stop
dress eggs desk	three days, fat man, three forks	ice-cream beans sea	crowd cows
u	**a—e**	**ing**	**igh**
bus buns drum	gate case snake	sleeping cooking	midnight, letter, turn right
jug cups sun	plate cake spade	jumping eating	light, dinner, turn left
ck	**i—e**	**ur**	**a (ar/ă)**
sock duck neck	five spoon tree	church, five men, seat	bath grass path
clock stick black dog	nine slide pig	three girls, turkey, fur coat	No, father. No, nasty.
ee	**o—e**	**aw**	**o(ŭ)**
feet nest tree	toe rope cake	claws jaw nose	No, mother.
legs sweets bed	bike nose bone	saw lawn toe	No, brother.
oo	**u—e**	**oi**	**y(ī)**
moon foot mug	smoke three fish	coin coins point	nine sky five
spoons feet roof	sheep tube case	oil can, teeth, claws	fly light slide
ar	**ai**	**er**	**ow (ō)**
car pram tarts	rain train snails	winter	high low (windows)
stars scarf foot	snail, tail, three tails	September	low high (walls)

Proof-Reading

The proof-reading exercises at the end of each sheet will be drawing only on points taught in Fat Sam.

Once again, there may be a small group who will need to be "talked through" the exercises, until they are ready to cope alone.

All could mark the passages with a red pencil. In this instance, *they* are the teachers. Proof-reading skills play an essential part in all writing and therefore children will benefit from acquiring them early. Encourage them to use these skills in their personal writing.

It is probably desirable that the worksheets should follow the week after the relevant word family in Fat Sam has been taught, the teaching points covered and the dictation given. The previous week's work will therefore be reinforced whilst the new work is in progress.

In a remedial situation, either group or 1-1, the same should apply. The worksheet should be discussed in the lesson, and perhaps a sentence built with plastic letters, the week *following* the teaching of the word family. The sheet could then be tackled in class, or at home.

Violet Brand

Sad Gran

Gran is sad.
The bad cat sat on her hat.
It is flat.

1. Choose a colour. Draw a line under the words in the 'a' family.
2. Can you draw a picture of Sad Gran?
3. Can you draw a picture of the bad cat and the flat hat?
4. Can you write about the hat?

  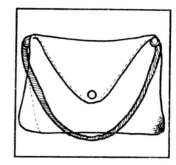

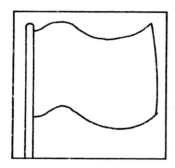  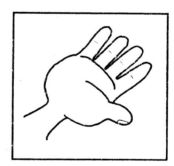

5. Write the words under the pictures.
   Colour the pictures.
6. **What is wrong?**
   The man has the flag, the bag and the tap in his bat.

Sad Gran and the doll

Sad Gran had a soft doll in a box. The bad cat got the doll from the box and lost it.

1. <u>Choose a colour. Draw a line under the words in the 'o' family.</u>
2. <u>Can you draw a picture of the bad cat and the doll?</u>
3. Can you draw a picture of Sad Gran and the box?
4. Can you write a sentence about the doll?

  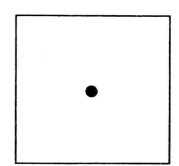

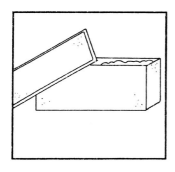  

5. <u>Write the words under the pictures.</u>
   Colour the pictures.
6. **What is wrong?**
   The cot is in the dog and the box is in the fox.

Sad Gran and the pigs

i

Sad Gran had six pigs. The big fox and the bad cat bit the pigs. Sad Gran hit the bad cat. The big fox ran off.

1. Choose a colour. Draw a line under the words in the 'i' family.
2. Can you draw a picture of the pigs?
3. Can you draw a picture of the fox, the bad cat and Sad Gran?
4. Can you write a sentence about the big fox and Sad Gran?

 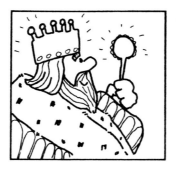 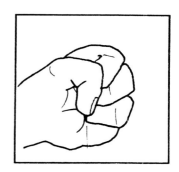

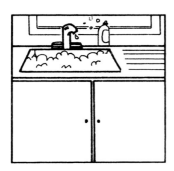 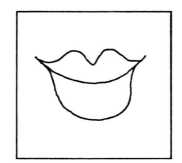 

5. Write the words under the pictures.
   Colour the pictures.
6. **What is wrong?**
   The kings six sat on the hill.

Sad Gran and the tent

The bad cat went to the red tent. He slept on the top of the bed. Sad Gran went to rest her legs on the bed. She fell on top of the bad cat and was cross.

1. <u>Choose a colour.</u> Draw a line under the words in the 'e' family.
2. <u>Can you draw a picture of the bad cat in the tent?</u>
3. Can you draw a picture of Sad Gran and the bad cat?
4. Can you write a sentence about Sad Gran's bed?

  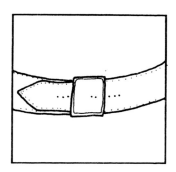

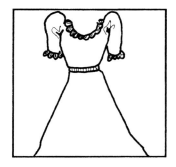  

5. <u>Write the words under the pictures.</u>
   Colour the pictures.
6. **What is wrong?**
   The dress is on top of the dask. It has a blet.

6

The bad cat and the mud

Sad Gran sits in the sun. The bad cat jumps in the soft mud and rubs the mud on his legs. He jumps on Sad Gran's lap.

1. Choose a colour. Draw a line under the words in the 'u' family.
2. Can you draw a picture of the bad cat in the mud?
3. Can you draw a picture of Sad Gran in the sun?
4. Can you write a sentence about the mud and Sad Gran?

  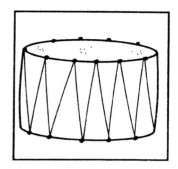

5. Write the words under the pictures.
   Colour the pictures.
6. **What is wrong?**
   The mun is on top of the bas. The bus stops and the man off gets.

Sad Gran is cross

Sad Gran smacks the back of the bad cat. He runs off to lick his milk. The mud sticks to Sad Gran and she picks it off. She is hot and cross.

1. <u>Choose a colour.</u> Draw a line under the words in the 'ck' family.
2. <u>Can you draw a picture of the mud on Sad Gran?</u>
3. Can you draw a picture of the bad cat and the milk?
4. Can you write a sentence about cross Sad Gran?

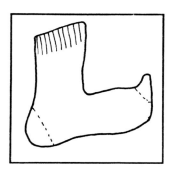

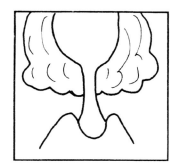

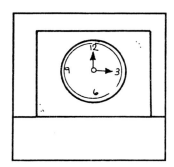
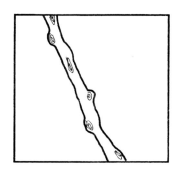

5. <u>Write the words under the pictures.</u>
   Colour the pictures.
6. **What is wrong?**
   Sox ducks get stuck in the blick mud. A men helps to lif them back into the pond.

Sad Gran and the Fat Man

The bad cat is at the top of the tree. Sad Gran sleeps in the hot sun. The bad cat sees the fat man, jumps from the tree and runs to meet him. The fat man picks up the bad cat, but Sad Gran keeps sleeping. She has not seen him.

1. <u>Choose a colour.</u> Draw a line under the words in the 'ee' family.
2. <u>Can you draw a picture of the bad cat in the tree?</u>
3. Can you draw a picture of the bad cat and the fat man?
4. Can Sad Gran see the fat man?

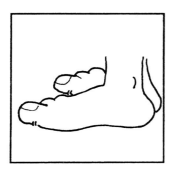 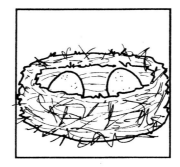 

5. <u>Write the words under the pictures.</u> (There may be a trick.)
   Colour the pictures.
6. **What is wrong?**
   The man sees the bus and runs to the bos stup. he meets a blak dog. It jumps up stops him.

The bad cat feels good

The bad cat sits on Sad Gran's foot. She looks up and sees the fat man.

"Oh, good," she says. "I will soon cook lots of hot food, if you will keep the bad cat from me."

The fat man picks up the bad cat. The bad cat looks at him and licks his hand. The cat feels good, not bad, as the fat man hugs him.

1. Choose a colour. Draw a line under the words in the 'oo' family.
2. Can you draw a picture of the bad cat on Sad Gran?
3. Can you draw a picture of Sad Gran cooking the food?
4. Can you write a sentence about a lick and a hug?

 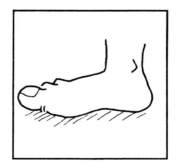 

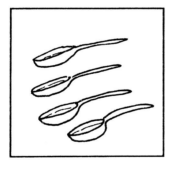 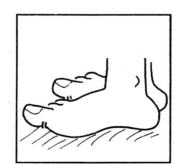 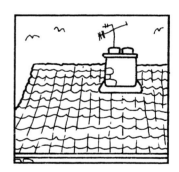

5. Write the words under the pictures. (There may be a trick.)

   Colour the pictures.

6. **What is wrong?**

   The spon is in the mug. The man piks up the moog and drops it his foot. it is too hot.

Sad Gran and the jam tart

Sad Gran's jam tart is good and the fat man licks his lips. It is dark and he must soon go back across the park to bed.

The bad cat jumps on his lap.

"No," said Sad Gran. "The cat must not jump up."

The fat man hugs the cat.

"I must go back across the park to sleep," he said.

Sad Gran packs the rest of the tart in a bag for the fat man.

1. Choose a colour. Draw a line under the words in the 'ar' family.
2. Can you draw a picture of Sad Gran and the jam tart?
3. Can you draw a picture of the fat man crossing the park in the dark?
4. Has the fat man got a bag in his hand?

  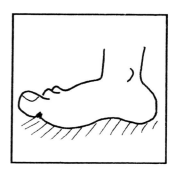

5. Write the words under the pictures.

   Colour the pictures.

6. **What is wrong?**

   The parm is on the man's foot and he dops the jam trt. It sticks to sock.

The Storm

Sad Gran cannot sleep and gets up. The storm stops her from sleeping. She looks at the clock. It is too soon to get up. She has a drink and a snack of pork and crisps. She forgets the storm and gets back into bed to sleep.

The bad cat cannot sleep and creeps from his box. He gets the rest of the pork for himself. Sad Gran will be cross in the morning.

1. Choose a colour. Draw a line under the words in the 'or' family.
2. Can you draw a picture of the storm?
3. Can you draw a picture of Sad Gran getting up?
4. Why will Sad Gran be cross?

  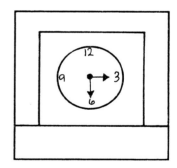

5. Write the words under the pictures. (There may be a trick.)
   Colour the pictures.

6. **What is wrong?**

   The man and the hors run in form the storm The forg jumps back into the pond.

Sad Gran and the fish man

Sad Gran gets up in the morning and looks at the dish.

"The bad cat has had the pork. I must rush to the shop and get fish," she says.

She runs across the park to the shop. The shop is shut, but a man sells fish from a van. She runs to the van.

"I need fish to cook. The bad cat has had the pork," she tells the man in the fish van.

"He is a bad, bad cat," says the fish man as he gets the fish for Sad Gran.

1. Choose a colour. Draw a line under the words in the 'sh' family.

2. Can you draw a picture of Sad Gran at the shop?

3. Can you draw a picture of the fish man and his van?

4. Why must Sad Gran rush across the park?

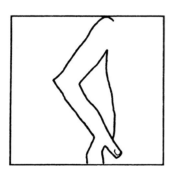

5. Write the words under the pictures. (There may be a trick.)

   Colour the pictures.

6. **What is wrong?**

   The fish big is no the dish in the shop, but the shup is shot.

The bad cat is sick

The bad cat creeps from his box and runs into the park. He sees a bag of fish and chips and starts to munch. The fish is bad and the chips look green. He feels sick.

Sad Gran runs back across the park. She has the fish from the van in a bag. She sees the bad cat. He looks sick. She sees the bad fish and the green chips.

"Good," she says. "The bad cat has had too much food. Let him sit in the park and be sick."

The fat man sees the bad cat and rubs his neck with his fat hand.
"You bad cat," he says. "You pinch too much food."

1. Choose a colour. Draw a line under the words in the 'ch' family.

2. Can you draw a picture of the bad cat with the fish and chips?

3. Can you draw a picture of the bad cat and the fat man?

4. Why is the bad cat sick?

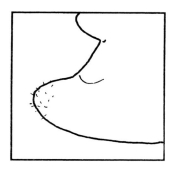  

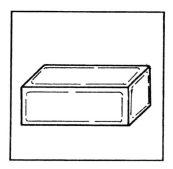  

5. Write the words under the pictures. (Think before you write.)

   Colour the pictures.

6. **What is wrong?**

   The man dops the gren mug and chips it. he pick it up.

Sad Gran forgets

Sad Gran runs in with the fish.

"I must have a drink of milk and then I will cook the fish for lunch," she thinks.

She has three mugs of milk and then cuts the fish into three. She gets a dish for it. With the fish in the dish, she thinks she needs fat on it. She looks for the fat.

"Oh no," she says. "I forgot to get the fat. I must rush back across the park to the man with the van."

As she runs off, the bad cat creeps back and sees the fish in the dish.

1. Choose a colour. Draw a line under the words in the **'th'** family.

2. Can you draw a picture of the fish in the dish?

3. Can you draw a picture of Sad Gran and the bad cat?

4. Write a sentence about Sad Gran's drink.

5. Write the words under the pictures. (Think before you write.)

   Colour the pictures.

6. **What is wrong?**

   The thin man has three dog. he needs lot of food of them.

The bad cat takes the fish

Sad Gran came back with the fat. No fish is in the dish.

"I left the fish in the dish," she thinks. "I cut it into three and went for the fat, but no fish is left."

She makes a hot drink in a mug and sits on the bench.

"It must be that bad cat," she thinks. "He makes me so cross. I will shake him, if I get him."

Thin Jim came to the gate with fish and chips on a plate.

"Take the fish and chips," he said. "Sam can get fat and you can get fat, but I shall not get fat."

Thin Jim gave Sad Gran his fish and chips.

1. Choose a colour. Draw a line under the words in the cake family.

2. Can you draw a picture of the dish and the bad cat?

3. Can you draw a picture of Thin Jim at the gate?

4. Will Thin Jim get fat?

 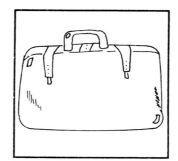 

  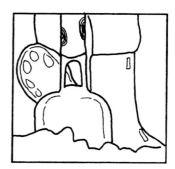

5. Write the words under the pictures.

   Colour the pictures.

6. **What is wrong?**

   The fate man has the cak on the plat, but the thin mane has no cak.

The red ice-pop

Sad Gran had nine bites of fish and five chips.

"I like Thin Jim's fish and chips," she said. Just then, Fat Sam came to the gate on his bent bike. The cat sat on the back.

Fat Sam got off his bike. He said to the bad cat, "Sit still. I will take this nice red ice-pop to Sad Gran."

He took the nice, red ice-pop to Sad Gran. "I do not like red ice-pops," said Sad Gran. "Thin Jim gave me fish and chips and they are nice."

Fat Sam went back to his bent bike and the bad cat.

"I will get Sad Gran a nice green ice-pop," he said.

1. Choose a colour. Draw a line under the words in the 'five' family.

2. Can you draw a picture of Fat Sam on his bike?

3. Can you draw a picture of Fat Sam and the ice-pop?

4. What did Sad Gran like?

 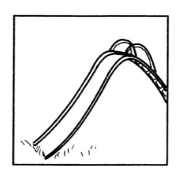 

5. Write the words under the pictures. (Think before you write.)

   Colour the pictures.

6. **What is wrong?**

   Fiv men wet to the big tree to get nin pigs. the pigs had run form the farm.

Sad Gran smells smoke

Fat Sam rode his bent bike home with the bad cat on the back.

Sad Gran began to smell smoke. She gave her nose a rub.

"Smoke," she said. "I can smell smoke." She went to the gate to look. The smoke came from the fish man's van.

"I must rush to tell the fish man," she said. As she ran, she hit her big toe on a log and sat on a bench to look.

Just then, Fat Sam rode back on his bent bike. He had a green ice-pop in his hand.

"Smoke, can you smell smoke, Sam?" yelled Sad Gran. "Tell the fish man he has smoke in his van." Fat Sam gave Sad Gran the green ice-pop and said, "Go back home, Gran and I will ride on my bike to the fish van."

1. <u>Choose a colour.</u> Draw a line under the words in the 'n<u>o</u>s<u>e</u>' family.
2. Can you draw a picture of Sad Gran and the smoke?
3. Can you draw a picture of Fat Sam on his bike with the ice-pop?
4. Write a sentence about Sad Gran and her toe.

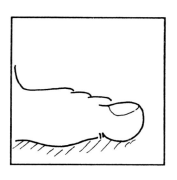 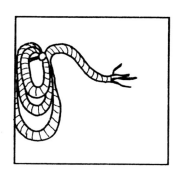 

  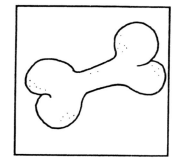

5. <u>Write the words under the pictures.</u> (Think before you write.)

   Colour the pictures.

6. **What is wrong?**

   The man fell form the tree. he broke his nos, his am and his big toe.

18

Thin Jim and the bad joke

Sad Gran sat on the bench and began to suck the green ice-pop. It was June and the sun was hot. She began to hum a nice tune.

Thin Jim came up and sat on the bench with Sad Gran.

"That Fat Sam makes up bad jokes," Thin Jim said. "He rode up to the fish man on his bent, blue bike and said rude things. Smoke in the fish van indeed. There cannot be smoke in the fish van."

"Did the fish man go back to his van said Sad Gran.

"No," said Thin Jim. "It is too hot for bad jokes. The fish man had a big bite of his ice and Fat Sam rode off on his bent blue bike."

1. Choose a colour. Draw a line under the words in the 'blue' family.

2. Can you draw a picture of Sad Gran on the bench?

3. Can you draw a picture of Fat Sam with the fishman?

4. Did Fat Sam have a red, or a green bike?

 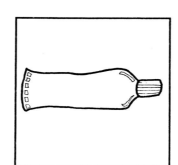 

5. Write the words under the pictures. (Think before you write.)

   Colour the pictures.

6. **What is wrong?**

   In jun the men went for a swim in the pond blue. The did not see the thee gren fish.

The bad cat and the pain in his tail

"Wait," said Sad Gran. "It is not a joke. Go back to the fish man and tell him."

Thin Jim got up from the bench and stood on a snail. He felt cross with Fat Sam and Sad Gran. "I will not go back," he said. "There is no smoke."

He went off in his big, red car. Sad Gran stood up, but she did not wave to Thin Jim. She felt the pain in her big toe and sat back on the bench to wait for Fat Sam.

Then he came on his bent bike. He was hot and black. The paint on his bike was black, not blue.

"The van is safe," he said. "The fish man is glad, but the bad cat is sad. He is in pain. His tail got stuck on a hot rail."

"I am glad that the fish van is safe," said Sad Gran, "but I am sad for the bike. It is black and needs blue paint."

"I am sad for the bad cat with a pain in his tail," said Fat Sam.

1. Choose a colour. Draw a line under the words in the 'ai' family.

2. Can you draw a picture of Thin Jim in his car?

3. Can you draw a picture of Fat Sam on his bike?

4. Can you write about the bad cat and his tail?

5. Write the words under the pictures. (Think before you write.)

   Colour the pictures.

6. **What is wrong?**

   the train is late And the man has to wait in the ran. he is cros.

Soap for Fat Sam oa

The bad cat began to groan.

"I will take the bad cat home across the road," said Fat Sam. "He can sleep in his box."

"You must have soap for your hands and the bike. I will get it for you," said Sad Gran.

Fat Sam, Sad Gran and the bad cat went across the road.

The bad cat sat in his box. He began to lick his tail and groan with pain. Fat Sam gave him a soft coat to sit on.

"Take this soap, Sam, with a cloth and the pail," said Sad Gran. "Get the black smoke from your blue bike and your hands. I will cut the loaf and make lots of toast."

Fat Sam gave the bad cat a quick pat and took the soap, the pail and the cloth from Sad Gran.

1. Choose a colour. Draw a line under the words in the 'oa' family.
2. Can you draw a picture of the bad cat in his box?
3. Can you draw a picture of Fat Sam with the pail?
4. Why did Sad Gran cut the loaf?

 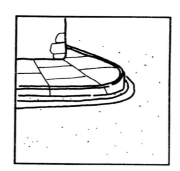 

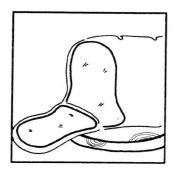  

5. Write the words under the pictures.
   Colour the pictures.
6. **What is wrong?**
   a b e f c d h g i

The black toast

First Fat Sam began to scrub the dirt from his hands with soap. Then he began to scrub the black dirt from his bent, blue bike. The dirt got onto his hands and his shirt.

"Wait," said Sad Gran. "The dirt is on your shirt. I will get the dirt from the bike. I will not get it on my skirt."

Fat Sam began to scrub the dirt from his hands with the soap. Sad Gran began to brush the black dirt from the blue bike. The bad cat sat on the coat in his box and gave a big groan.

Sad Gran had left the toast on the grill.

"Smoke," yelled Fat Sam. "I can see smoke."

The smoke came from the toast on the grill. The toast was black.

1. Choose a colour. Draw a line under the words in the 'ir' family.

2. Can you draw a picture of the dirt on Fat Sam's shirt?

3. Can you draw a picture of the toast on the grill?

4. Can you write sentences about your pictures?

5. Write the words under the pictures.

   Colour the pictures.

6. **What is wrong?**

   B C E F A I G H

A big black cloud

Sad Gran gave a loud shout. She ran to the grill and took off the black toast. It was hot.

"Ouch. The toast is hot. It must go out of the house," she said.

She took the hot, black toast outside for the birds. "That's a big, black cloud," she said to Fat Sam. "The cloud is black, the bike is black, the toast is black and my hands are black. I must have the soap, Sam." She found the soap and began to scrub her hands in the sink. It began to rain.

"Good," said Sad Gran. "The rain will make the bike blue again. I will make the toast."

1. <u>Choose a colour. Draw a line under the words in the 'ou' family.</u>
2. <u>Can you draw a picture of Fat Sam and Sad Gran with all of the black things?</u>
3. Can you write sentences about your picture?

4. <u>Write the words under the pictures.</u>
   Colour the pictures.

5. **What is wrong?**
   a b c d f g h i g l m n p q r t u v x y z

Fat Sam is cross

ea(ē)

Sad Gran made the tea and the toast and Fat Sam came in to eat his tea.

"Let us have jam and cream with the toast," said Fat Sam.

"No," said Sad Gran. "You are too fat. You can have jam, but no cream."

Fat Sam did not like jam and toast without cream. Just then, Thin Jim came to the house. He gave Sad Gran a big bag of peas and beans.

"Have peas and beans with meat," he said. "You will not get fat with them."

Fat Sam was cross. He did not like peas and beans with meat, but he did like cream for tea. He went outside to look for the bad cat.

He gave a shout, as the bad cat ran round the house with a mouse in his mouth.

1. Choose a colour. Draw a line under the words in the 'ea' family.
2. Can you draw a picture of Thin Jim at the house?
3. Can you draw a picture of the bad cat and the mouse?
4. Did Sad Gran give Fat Sam cream for tea?

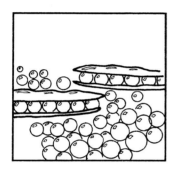 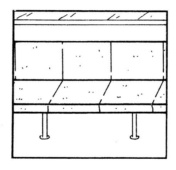 

5. Write the words under the pictures.

   Colour the pictures.

6. **What is wrong?**

   A B D C E F H I K M N O Q R T U W X Y Z

24

The bad cat and the mouse

The bad cat ran into the house with the mouse in his mouth.

"Take that mouse away, you bad cat," shouted Sad Gran.

"Sam, make this cat take the mouse away. He must not play with it in the house."

Fat Sam began to chase the bad cat.

"I must not stay," said Thin Jim. "On Tuesday, I go away on holiday."

Thin Jim went home to pack his car for his holiday and Fat Sam began to puff and pant.

"That bad cat still has the mouse in the house. I think he will have to stay," he said.

"Oh no he will not," said Sad Gran.

"You go away today. Go back across the park with your bike and stay away. I will get the bad cat and the mouse."

1. Choose a colour. Draw a line under the 'ay' words.

2. Can you draw a picture of Fat Sam and the bad cat in the house?

3. Can you draw a picture of Thin Jim packing his car?

4. Can the bad cat and Fat Sam stay in the house?

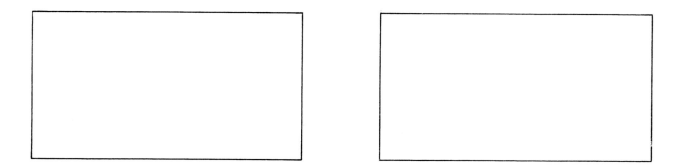

5. Write down six words in the 'ay' family.

6. **What is wrong?**

on tuesday jim will go away on holday. he will say in a hous by the sea.

Fat Sam takes a bite

Fat Sam is sad. He has had no tea. He stands looking at the jam and the toast, as Sad Gran chases the bad cat.

Fat Sam takes a big bite of toast. He takes three bites and jam is round his mouth, but he is dreaming of cream on the toast.

Sad Gran stands looking at him.

"That is the way to get fat, Sam," she says. "You can stay and I will cook the peas and beans, with meat."

"I am not staying for Thin Jim's peas and beans. I like food that makes me fat," said Fat Sam, stamping out of the house.

Soon, he was standing at the gate with his bent, blue bike. He sees the bad cat playing with the mouse.

"You can stay with the mouse," he says to the bad cat, "but I am not staying and eating Thin Jim's food."

1. <u>Choose a colour.</u> Draw a line under the 'ing' words.
2. <u>Can you draw a picture of Fat Sam and the toast?</u>
3. Write a sentence under the picture.
4. Can you draw a picture of Fat Sam stamping out of the house?

5. <u>What is the girl doing?</u>
6. **What is wrong?**

today is sunday and the grils are look at the sea.

No holiday for Sad Gran

Gran is sad. It is Thursday and Thin Jim is away on holiday. He went away on Tuesday and will not be back until Saturday. Sad Gran will not have a turn for a holiday.

She has no car and the train costs too much. She cannot go and sit on the beach by the sea.

She looks across the park to the church and sees Fat Sam on his bent, blue bike. He has not been to see her for three days.

He rides across to Sad Gran and says, "Will you come to my house? My wife is cooking a big turkey for us to eat with peas and beans."

"Oh, yes please," said Sad Gran, "but my feet hurt and your house is a long way."

"Sit on the back of my bike, and I will give you a ride," said Fat Sam.

1. Choose a colour. Draw a line under the 'ur' words.

2. Draw a picture of Sad Gran on Fat Sam's bike?

3. Can you write about the picture?

  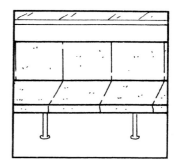

4. Write the words under the pictures?

5. **Which letters are missing?** Put them in.

   A B D E F H J K L N O P R S T V X Y Z

Bump on the lawn

Fat Sam's bike went bump, bump, bump across the lawn. Sad Gran went bump, bump, bump on the back. Her jaw went bang, bang, bang on her chest and her teeth hurt.

She saw the bad cat run up to the bike and put its claw on Fat Sam's leg.

She gave a shout as the bike hit the bad cat. She fell off onto the lawn and Fat Sam fell on top of her.

Sad Gran was shouting, "Get off, Sam, Get off." Fat Sam began to crawl off.

"That bad, bad cat," he said. "Just wait until I get my hands on him."

"I cannot eat turkey. My teeth and jaw hurt too much. I will crawl back into bed. You go home to your wife," said Sad Gran.

She began to crawl across the lawn to the house when she saw the bad cat.

"Take that cat with you," she said.

1. Choose a colour. Draw a line under the **'aw'** words.

2. Draw a picture of Sad Gran, Fat Sam and the bike on the lawn.

3. Write about the picture.

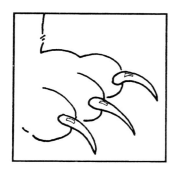 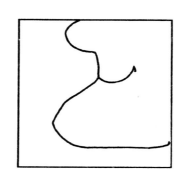 

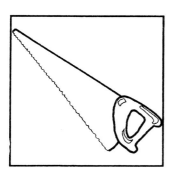  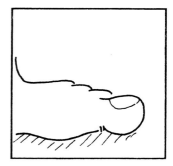

4. Write the words under the pictures.

5. **What is wrong?**

on saturday they went to the shops. they not go on tuesday, wednesday and thursday.

Fat Sam took the bad cat and went back to join his wife. She was cross with Fat Sam.

"Sad Gran on the bent bike! You must be mad and she must feel ill." she said, as she took the turkey from the cooking oil and put it on a big, round plate. She put the peas and beans on to boil.

Then, a noise at the gate made her look up. She saw Sad Gran crawling across the lawn to the house.

"Can I join you?" said Sad Gran. "My toes hurt, my jaw hurts, my teeth hurt and the point of my nose hurts, but I do like turkey.

"Did you crawl across the park?" said Fat Sam.

"No," said Sad Gran. "The fish man gave me a lift in his van. He gave me a jar of cooking oil for you."

Sad Gran was pointing at a large jar of cooking oil at the gate.

1. Choose a colour. Draw a line under the 'oi' words.

2. Draw a picture of Sad Gran on the lawn.

3. Write about the picture.

  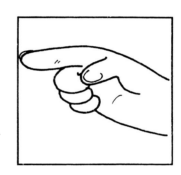

 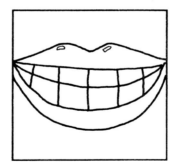 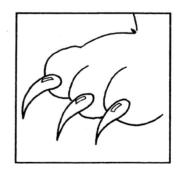

4. Write the words under the pictures.

5. **What is wrong?**

the thee cons fell into the ol can. the man tok a stik with a pint on it to get them out.

Fat Sam drops the oil

"Get the cooking oil from the gate, Sam," said his wife.

She put her hands under Sad Gran's arms and helped her into the house.

"We are glad you have come to join us for supper," she said. "Sit beside me. The turkey is out of the tin and the peas and beans are boiling."

Sad Gran smiled and said, "That's good. Yesterday I had a letter from my sister. She is going on holiday to the seaside in September."

"That's nice for her," said Fat Sam's wife. "It's better than a winter holiday in November."

There was a loud noise outside. Crash!

She jumped up and ran out of the house. Fat Sam was sitting in cooking oil on the lawn.

"I dropped the jar," he said.

1. Choose a colour. Draw a line under the 'er' words.
2. Draw a picture of Fat Sam in the cooking oil?
3. Write about the picture.?
4. Look at the pictures.

   Is it winter or summer?

   Is it September or November?

5. Look at the pictures.
6. **What is wrong?**

   yesday i had fish and chips for diner and eg and chips for super.

"I can see you dropped the jar," said Fat Sam's wife, "but did you have to fall in the oil?"

"I slipped in the oil," said Fat Sam.

Sad Gran came into the hall and held on to the wall.

"Did Sam fall?" she asked.

"Yes," said Fat Sam. "I did fall. A girl's ball hit the jar of oil and I dropped it. The girl ran away and I slipped in the oil."

"Get up," said his wife. He put his hand on a small wall and got up. Oil dripped from his shirt and went on her skirt.

"Go in the back way with all that oil," she said.

He began to creep across the lawn. He held onto the small wall.

Poor Fat Sam. First the bad cat made him fall off his bike with Sad Gran and then the girl with the ball made him drop the jar of oil. He has bad luck all the time.

1. <u>Choose a colour. Draw a line under '**all**' words.</u>

2. <u>Draw a picture of Sad Gran, Fat Sam's wife and Fat Sam as he gets up from the oil.</u>

3. Write about the picture.

4. Did Fat Sam have good luck, or bad luck?

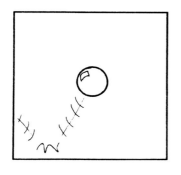 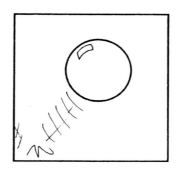 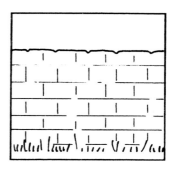

  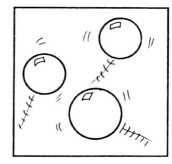

5. <u>Write two words under each picture.</u>

6. **What is wrong?**

   a leter came yesday form my sister. she will cal to see me in november.

Fat Sam cuts the turkey

Fat Sam is sitting waiting for the turkey with plenty of peas and beans. He has on a clean shirt and his wife has a clean skirt. She is cutting a nice crusty loaf. She seems a bit grumpy about the cooking oil.

Sad Gran is not grumpy. She smiles and is happy. She has a hot milky drink and waits for the turkey.

"Cut the turkey, Sam." said his wife. "I am cutting the crusty loaf.

Fat Sam starts to cut plenty of turkey. The skin is nice and crispy and he eats small bits as he cuts.

The bad cat creeps in and Fat Sam drops crispy bits for him.

"Stop it," shouted Sad Gran. "I saw that. Send that bad cat away."

Fat Sam looked quickly at Sad Gran and cut his hand, not the turkey. He cut it badly. His hand was red, the plate was red and the turkey was red.

1. <u>Choose a colour.</u> Draw a line under 'y' saying 'ē' at the end of words.
2. <u>Draw a picture of Fat Sam and his wife cutting.</u>
3. Write about the picture.

4. <u>How is Gran looking?</u>
5. **What is wrong?**

   my siser is hapy. in septber she will away holday.

Fat Sam's cut hand   ea (ĕ)

The bleeding from Fat Sam's hand is heavy. Sad Gran said, "Turn on the tap."

She took Fat Sam to the sink and held his hand under the tap.

"Have a clean rag ready." She said to his wife. "Spread it out."

The bleeding stopped and Sad Gran saw that it was a small cut, instead of a big one.

"Look, Sam," she said. "Lift your head and look. It is not a big cut."

She took the soft, clean rag and put it round Fat Sam's hand.

"Sit down," she said. "Your wife will cut the turkey instead of the crusty bread and I will cut the bread instead of her."

Fat Sam sat down and held his head. "That bad cat brings me bad luck all the time," he groaned.

1. <u>Choose a colour</u>. Draw a line under the '**ea**' words that sound like 'red'. (There may be a trick).

2. <u>Draw a picture of Fat Sam and Sad Gran at the sink.</u>

3. Draw a picture of Fat Sam and the clean rag.

4. Did Sad Gran cut the turkey?

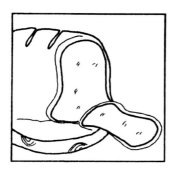 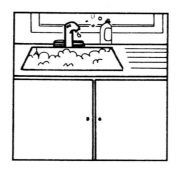 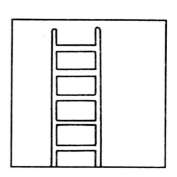

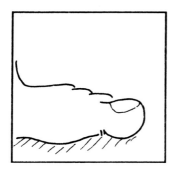 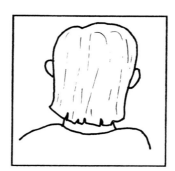 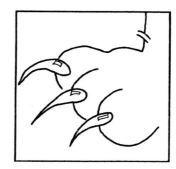

5. <u>Write the words under the pictures.</u>

6. **What is wrong?**

   jim went away on tusday. he will came back on satday. today is thurday.

The Bad Cat eats Sam's supper

ow

Now the turkey is ready and the peas and beans are ready. Sad Gran, Fat Sam and his wife sit down for supper. The turkey is crispy and brown. The peas and beans are fresh and green.

"How nice it is," said Sad Gran. "Did you get the turkey in town?"

"Yes. I'm glad it is good," said Fat Sam's wife.

"I went to town yesterday on the bus. There was such a crowd in the streets, but not in the shops."

"Did you come back on the bus?" asked Sad Gran.

"Yes, I did and the turkey was heavy," said Fat Sam's wife. "There was such a crowd on the bus that I did not sit down."

Fat Sam did not talk. He found it hard to eat his supper with just a fork. He had his bad hand down in his lap.

The peas began to fall down from his fork onto the carpet. Fat Sam felt cross. He liked to eat lots of food and now it was falling down instead of going into his mouth.

The bad cat was glad. He had crept in and was eating the peas and bits of meat as they fell down.

1. Choose a colour. Draw a line under the **'ow'** words that sound like 'cow'.

2. Draw a picture of Fat Sam's wife on the bus.

3. Write about the picture.

4. Draw a picture of Fat Sam dropping food

5. Write about the picture.

6. Write the words under the pictures.

7. **What is wrong?**

The turky is to big and to heavy to take on the bus. the bus is to crowdd.

34

In the park at midnight   igh

It was night when Sad Gran was ready to walk back to her house.

"Sam, you must go with Gran," said his wife. "It is not right for her to cross the park alone at midnight."

The moon was bright and gave light as they went back across the park.

"My right hand still hurts," said Fat Sam.

"My jaw hurts too," said Sad Gran. "That bad cat. Let him stay out of my sight.

"Let him stay out of my sight, too." said Fat Sam.

The moon was bright and gave lots of light, but they did not see the bad cat as he came back across the park at midnight. He stayed under the tall trees to the right of them.

Fat Sam and Sad Gran did not look to the right, nor to the left. They were looking at the gate at the end of the park.

1. Choose a colour. Draw a line under the **'igh'** words.

2. Draw a picture of Fat Sam, Sad Gran and the bad cat in the moon-light.

3. Write about the picture.

turn _____

turn _____

4. Write the words under the pictures.

5. **What is wrong?**

   At the lihts the cars must right. the blu car wnt lft.

35

The Shut Gate

Sad Gran and Fat Sam went along the path in the bright moon-light to the gate. Then they had a nasty shock. The gate was locked. It was midnight and rather late. Were they stuck in the park all night?

"Oh, Sam," said Sad Gran. "It will be nasty on the damp grass in the park all night."

"Let me think," said Fat Sam. "There must be a way out." Sad Gran began to moan. "I want a nice hot bath and a nice soft bed, not a hard bench in the park."

"Let me think," said Sam.

It was rather hard to think at midnight, with a hand that hurt. He looked to the right and he looked to the left.

At last he saw the bad cat creeping across the grass to a big hole in the railings.

"Look, Gran," he said. "The bad cat has saved us. There is a rather big hole in the railings.

Fat Sam and Sad Gran left the path and walked across the grass to the hole.

1. Choose a colour. Draw a line under the words in the 'a' family that sound like car. Read the words aloud and listen to the sound. (If the children say păth, remove this instruction before photocopying.)

2. Draw a picture of Sad Gran and Fat Sam at the gate and the bad cat at the hole.

3. Did Sad Gran want to stay in the park?

4. Is this mother?

5. Is she nice?

6. Write the words under the pictures.

7. **Can you put in the rest of the letters?**

A B   Y Z

Why me?

"I will try to lift you up in my arms Gran," said Thin Jim.

He took her by the arms and began to lift. Her feet came off the grass and onto the top of the railings.

"Jump Gran," said Thin Jim.

Sad Gran jumped and stood by Thin Jim on the dry path outside the park.

"Let us help you now, Sam," said Sad Gran.

"No thanks," said Fat Sam. "I will try to get out myself."

Sad Gran began to cry.

"I cannot go home to bed and let you stay stuck in the railings," she said.

"Why not?" asked Thin Jim. "The night is dry. There are no clouds in the sky. He can try to sleep until morning."

Thin Jim went off in his car and Sad Gran went back to her house to try and get some sleep.

"Why me?" asked Fat Sam. "Why do I have bad luck all the time?"

1. Choose a colour. Draw a line under the words in the 'cry' family.

2. Draw a picture of Sad Gran on the railings.

3. Draw a picture of Sad Gran and Thin Jim going off.

4. Will Fat Sam sleep?

 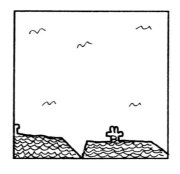 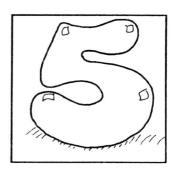

 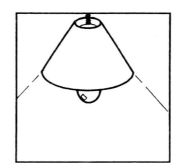 

5. Write the words under the pictures.

6. **What is wrong?**
   Wen did the girl go to the shop? wy did she go wat did she get.

7. Write down three question words.

Stuck in the railings

Sad Gran and Fat Sam stood in front of the hole in the railings.

"I will go first," said Fat Sam.

"It looks rather small for you, Sam," said Sad Gran. "I will go first."

"No," said Fat Sam and he stood in front of Sad Gran. He bent down by the hole in the railings. He put his head down and began to crawl. His head was outside the park, but his legs were inside the park. He was stuck.

"Oh, Sam," said Sad Gran. "I said the hole was too small. Is there no other way out of the park?"

"I wish I was thin like my brother," said Fat Sam.

"You are stuck in the fence until Monday morning," said Sad Gran, "and I am stuck in the park."

Just then, a car stopped in front of the park. It was Thin Jim back from his holiday.

"Can I help?" asked Thin Jim.

"Yes please," said Sad Gran.

"No thanks," said Fat Sam. "I will stay here."

1. Choose a colour. Draw a line under the words in the **'mother'** family.

2. Draw a picture of Fat Sam stuck in the fence.

3. Draw a picture of Thin Jim back from holiday.

4. Will Thin Jim help Fat Sam and Sad Gran?

5. Is this father?

6. Is this the sister?

7. Can you draw a son?

8. Which is the first school day in the week?

9. **What is wrong?**

   on monday i will to london on train with sam and jim. We will come hom on tuesday.

No Fat Sam

When Sad Gran woke up in the morning, she looked out of the bedroom window.

She looked across to the park railings. She looked high and she looked low. There was no Fat Sam. The railings were still there. The hole was still there and the yellow gate was still locked.

How did he get out?

Sad Gran went down to have a cup of tea. It was hot and she started to blow it.

Then she saw the bad cat at the gate. He gave a low cry. She stood and looked out of the window. There was Fat Sam on his bent, blue bike. "How did you get out?" she called.

"My wife came to look for me. She took my feet and gave three slow tugs. With the last tug, I was free," said Fat Sam. "My wife fell down on the grass with a nasty bump."

"I'm glad you came to tell me," said Sad Gran. "Have a cup of tea."

"Yes, please," said Fat Sam. "A cup of tea, but no toast. I will not grow fat, but will get thin like Jim."

"You will not grow fat and I will not be sad," said Gran.

1. <u>Choose a colour.</u> Draw a line under the words in the **'snow'** family. Read them aloud and listen for the right sound.

2. Draw a picture of Fat Sam's wife giving him a tug.

3. Draw your last picture of Fat Sam with Sad Gran.

4. Will Sad Gran stay sad?

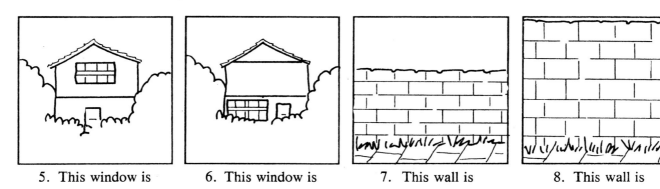

5. This window is   6. This window is   7. This wall is   8. This wall is

9. **What is wrong?**
   the yelow bath is dirt. wen will it be clean.

10. **Can you finish this?**
    a b c

11. **Can you finish this?**
    Sunday   M   T   Wednesday
    T   Friday   S